CW00810047

Unit 1

A Viking Raid

Sentence work

- To practise using active verbs

Verbs

The men are loading the boat.

Words like **loading** tell us what action is taking place. Words that tell about actions are active **verbs**.

Remember

Active verbs are sometimes called **doing words**.

1 Write a sentence to go with each picture. Underline the active verb in each sentence.

a 

b 

c 

d 

Helpful words

looking rowing waving pulling

2 Copy these sentences, but think of a better verb than those underlined:

a *Eric went excitedly down to the ship.*

b *The sailors got the heavy water barrel on to the boat.*

c *Astrid is worried she won't get enough food this winter.*

Helpful words

find ran lifted

Capital letters and full stops

Copy these sentences about the Viking expedition. Put in the missing capital letters and full stops.

1 a the food supplies were running low

b all the village children helped to prepare the boat

c the younger children were to stay at home

2 a eric was very proud of harald, his father

b eric lived with harald, his father, astrid, his mother, and his brothers and sisters in a viking village close to what we now call the north sea

c harald had said eric could go with him on the expedition

Sentence work

- To use capital letters to start sentences and for names
- To use full stops

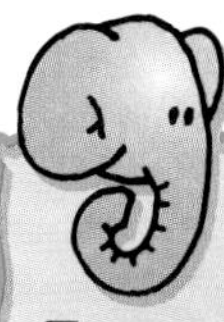

Remember

Every sentence must start with a **capital letter** and end with a **full stop**.

Proper nouns (special names) start with capital letters, too.

oi and *oy* words

1 Answer each of these puzzle questions with a different ***oi*** or ***oy*** word:

What is:

a a long sea journey, beginning with v?
b to make water very hot so it bubbles?
c things children like, beginning with t?
d comes from your mouth and begins with v?
e another name for a loud sound, beginning with n?

2 Write a sentence about Eric the Viking using each of these words:

point   boy   enjoy

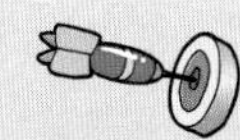

Word work

- To practise *oi* and *oy* spellings

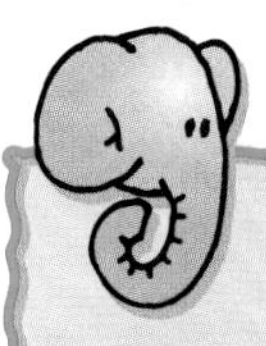

Remember

The letters ***oi*** and ***oy*** can make a similar sound.

Helpful words

noise   voice   toys
boil   voyage

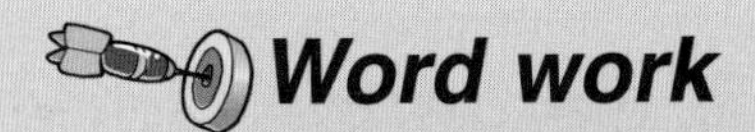

Word work

- To put words starting with the same letter into alphabetical order

Alphabetical order

a b c d e f g h i j k l m n o p q r s t u v w x y z

carrots potatoes spinach

Words are put in **alphabetical order** using their first letter.

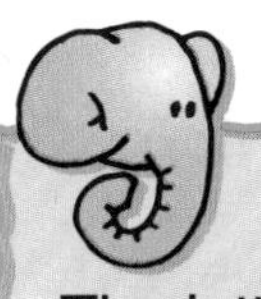

Remember

The letters in the alphabet are in **alphabetical order**.

1 Put these words in alphabetical order:

a red green yellow
b goat sheep cow
c hammer axe chopper
d Viking Saxon Roman

If a group of words all begin with the same letter, they are put in **alphabetical order** using their **second** letter.

a b c d e f g h i j k l m n o p q r s t u v w x y z

parsnip peas potatoes

Tip

Use a dictionary to help you.

2 Put these words in alphabetical order using their **second** letter:

a ship sail sea
b rope run rescue
c Eric Elfida Ethel
d whales water weather

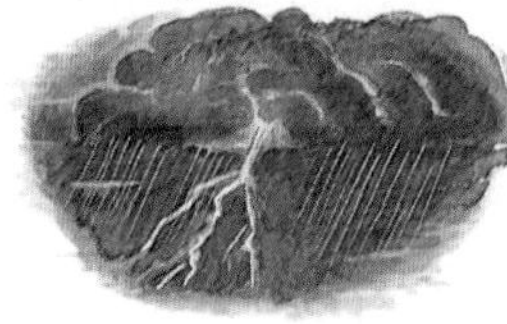

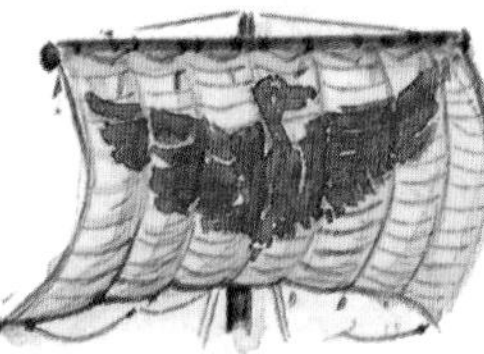

Handwriting

oi and *oy* patterns

oi oy oi oy oi oy oi oy oi oy oi oy

1 Neatly copy the letter patterns in the box three times.

2 Copy this silly sentence twice, as neatly as you can:

The coy boy enjoyed his noisy toys.

Two Lists

Present and past tenses

Sentence work

- To practise using present and past tenses

Most verbs ending with ***ing***, are happening at the **present time**:

Tommy is shopping.

If a verb ends with ***ed***, it has happened in the **past**:

Tommy walked to the shop.

1 a Write these verbs in the past tense.
The first is done to help you.

walk walked jump kick pull ask

b Now write the words in question 1a in the present tense.

walking

To make the **past tense** of *some* verbs, we don't add ***ed***. We need to change the word.

We are going to the shops.

We went to the shops.

Are you listening to what I'm saying?

Did you listen to what I said?

Helpful words

fell drank held
ran made

2 a Write the past tense of each of these verbs.
The first is done to help you.

drink drank

fall run make hold

b What is the present tense of each of these past tense verbs?

went came lost forgot

Tip

The poem *Two Lists* will help you to answer question 2b.

Sentence work

- To use commas in lists

Lists in sentences

We use commas between each item in a list, but we use **and** between the last two:

Dad asked Tommy to buy carrots, peas, bread and an apple pie.

Copy these sentences adding the missing commas:

1 a *I went shopping to buy some sweets a comic a drink and a paper for Mum.*

b *When I arrived home we had pizza beans sandwiches cake biscuits grapes and bananas for tea.*

2 *Dad told me not to talk to strangers to come straight home not to lose the change not to get lost and to be careful crossing the roads.*

Word work

- To learn the rules for adding *ing* and *ed*

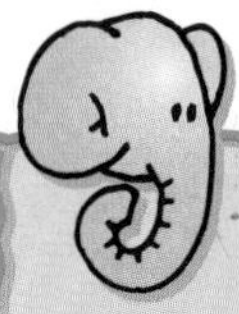

Remember

The vowel letters are **a e i o u.**

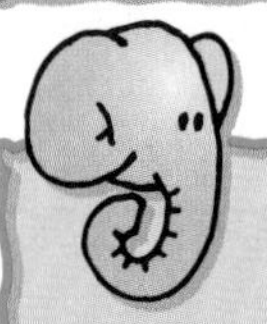

Remember

If there are *two* vowel letters before the last letter (like ***ee***), the last letter is *not* doubled before adding ***ing*** or ***ed***.

Adding *ing* and *ed*

Remember, if there is just one vowel letter *before* the last letter, the last letter is *doubled* before adding ***ing***:

shop shopping

1 Add *ing* to these words, like this:

run + ing = running

slip get hop hit

If the verb ends in *magic* e, the ***e*** is dropped when ***ing*** or ***ed*** is added:

stare stared staring

2 a Copy this table and fill the gaps.

b Add three more *magic e* words to the table.

Verb	+ ing	+ ed
smile		
grumble		
giggle		
change		
stroke		

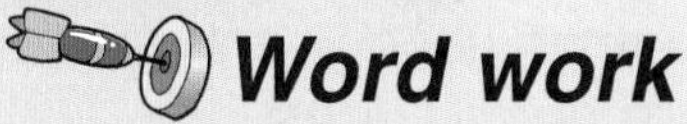

Word work

- To use similar words or phrases

Definitions

A **definition** explains the *meaning* of a word.

Here are some definitions of words found in the poem *Two Lists*:

stranger	someone you don't know
lost	unsure where you are
bread	a food made from flour, water and yeast
remember	keep it in your mind, don't forget

Tip

A **phrase** is a way of saying something.

1 Answer these questions:

a Which word means you are 'unsure where you are'?

b What is made from flour, water and yeast?

c What is the definition of a 'stranger'?

2 Write your own definitions of these words:
carrot road forget

ing pattern

Handwriting

ing ing ing ing ing ing ing ing ing ing

1 Neatly copy the letter pattern in the box three times.

2 Neatly write a funny sentence of your own that has all these words: singing bringing ringing dinging

The Day the Roof Fell In

Sentence work

- To learn how adverbs help verbs

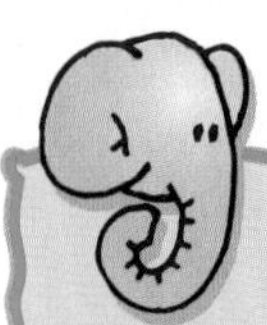

Remember

Adjectives tell us more about **nouns**.

Adverbs usually tell us more about **verbs**.

Tip

Adverbs tell us *how*, *when* or *where* the action of a verb takes place.

Many *how* adverbs end in ***ly***.

Adverbs

Adverbs tell us more about verbs:

A section of the roof <u>*unexpectedly*</u> *collapsed.*
adverb (unexpectedly) — verb (collapsed)

The **adverb** *unexpectedly* describes *how* the roof *collapsed*.

1 Make an adverb that ends in *ly* from each of these words:

quick <u>*quickly*</u> *slow* *strong* *weak*
stupid *poor* *clever* *foolish*

2 a Copy these sentences and write an adverb to fill each gap. The words in brackets will help you.

Some ladies (kind) wrapped the children in blankets to keep them warm.

The rescue services (quick) arrived at the school.

"It (unexpected) collapsed under the weight," said the fire chief.

Tip

Watch out for words that end in a ***y***!

Change the ***y*** to ***i*** before adding ***ly***.

b Use each of these pairs of words in a sentence:

angry angrily *happy happily* *kind kindly*

Using question marks

Remember to use a question mark to show when a sentence asks a question.

1 Copy just the question sentences. Add the question marks.

I am James, the reporter from the local paper.
Do you go to Nuffield Primary School
Were you in one of the rooms that was flooded
I expect you were frightened.
Why did it happen

2 Imagine that you are James Matthews, the reporter. Write three more questions you could have asked on the day the roof collapsed.

Sentence work

- To practise using question marks

Tip

A **?** has a full stop built into it.

Remember

You must finish each question with a question mark.

Suffix – *ness*

The fire services reported a weak<u>ness</u> in the school roof which led to the collapse.

When the suffix ***ness*** is added to most words ending in ***y***, the ***y*** is changed to an ***i***:

heavy + <u>ness</u> = heav<u>i</u>ness

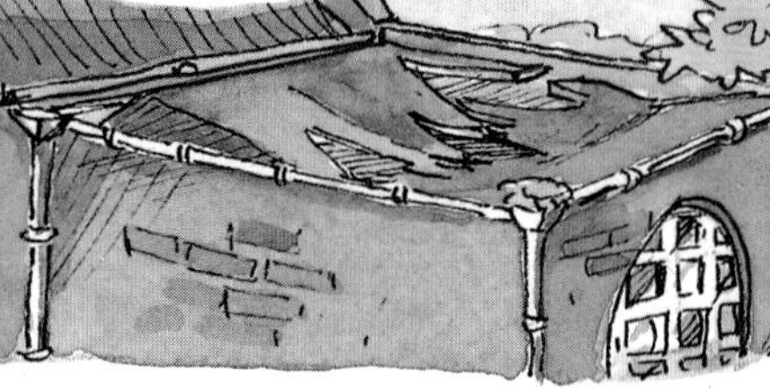

1 Add the suffix *ness* to each of these words:

dark	*sore*	*happy*
lazy	*ill*	*nasty*
empty	*busy*	*like*

2 Write at least four more words that have the *ness* suffix.

Word work

- To learn about changing *y* to *i* before *ness*

Word work

- To learn more about compound words

Compound words

When two small words are used to make one bigger word, it is called a **compound word**.

1 Choose a word from each column to make a compound word:

book	work
tooth	case
fire	fall
egg	brush
water	cup

Helpful words

waterfall eggcup firework toothbrush bookcase

2 Write as many compound words as you can that begin with:

fire farm cross

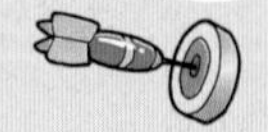

Handwriting

ully pattern

ully ully ully ully ully ully ully ully ully

1 Neatly copy the letter pattern in the box three times.

2 Neatly copy these words, adding the suffix *fully* to each one. Like this:

care carefully

grace wonder pain shame hope

Fetch the Slipper

Powerful verbs

Grandad looked.

Grandad scowled.

Scowled is a more **powerful verb** than *looked*.
The reader gets a better idea of how very cross Grandad felt!

Sentence work

- To think about using more powerful verbs

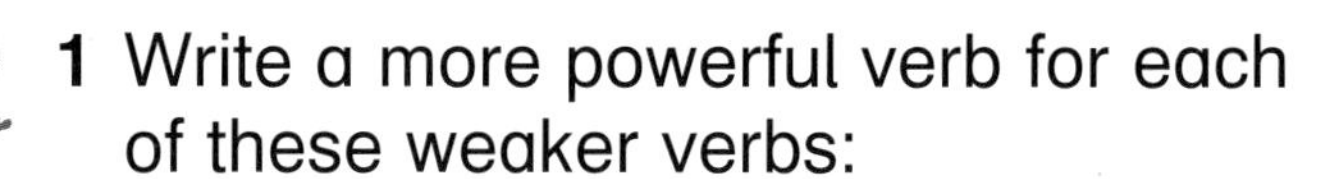

1 Write a more powerful verb for each of these weaker verbs:

call *scream*   walk   use   take   run

Helpful words

sprint operate scream
grab hobble grasp

2 Copy these sentences, changing the verb (underlined) for a stronger one:

a *Jamie went up the stairs two at a time.*

b *Benbow came in the front door.*

c *He went across to Grandad.*

d *"Get down, you horrible dog!" said Grandad.*

e *"Did you hear what Grandad called our lovely dog?" said the children to Mum.*

Helpful words

shouted leapt
charged muttered
bounced

Commas

Sentence work

- To use commas to mark pauses in sentences

We use commas in sentences to tell the reader when to make a short pause.

It's one of my best velvet slippers, that Betty sent from America.

It's one of my best velvet slippers is the main part of the sentence.

that Betty sent from America. is an extra part, telling us about the slippers.

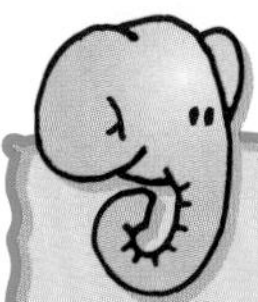

Remember

A sentence must make sense by itself.

1 Copy these sentences. Neatly underline the main part of each sentence, and put a comma where you think the reader should pause.

a *We all love Grandad even if he is rather grumpy.*

b *Our teacher says Benbow can come to school next week provided he behaves!*

c *My friends are all excited though Mum isn't sure it's a very sensible idea.*

2 Look in your reading book. Find two sentences that have commas. Write the main part of each sentence, that could be a sentence by itself.

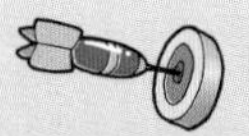

Word work

- To remember when to use *ow* and when to use *ou*

ow and *ou* words

Grandad sc<u>ow</u>led as Jamie and Fiona began to sh<u>ou</u>t for Benbow.

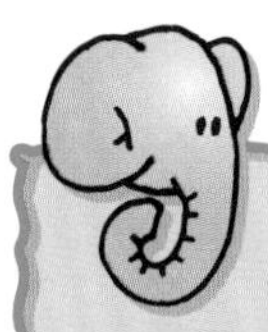

Remember

The letters ***ow*** and ***ou*** can make a similar sound.

1 Copy the sentences. Fill the gap with a correct ***ow*** or ***ou*** word.

a *Grandad came ________ looking grumpy.*

b *Grandad sat ________ on a chair at the kitchen table.*

c *Jamie and Fiona smiled when they saw the ________ on Grandad's face!*

d *Benbow was very muddy when he ran in from ________.*

e *Benbow looked all around the ________ for the slipper.*

Helpful words

frown outside down house downstairs

2 a Write three words with ***ow*** and three words with ***ou***. Check the words have a similar sound.

b Write as many of your ***ow*** and ***ou*** words as you can in one silly or funny sentence.

Suffix – *ment*

Word work

- To learn to spell some words with the suffix *ment*

1 a Add the suffix *ment* to each of these words:

enjoy____

pay____

treat____

agree____

punish____

entertain____

Tip

A **root word** is the smaller word the suffix is added to.

b Write three sentences. Use a word ending in ***ment*** in each one.

2 What is the root word of each of these words?

attachment agreement advertisement

replacement improvement encouragement

ou and *ow* patterns

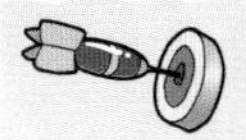

Handwriting

ou ow ou ow ou ow ou ow ou ow

1 Neatly copy the letter patterns in the box three times.

2 Neatly copy this silly sentence, then make up another using ***ou*** and ***ow*** words:

Our favourite clown frowned as he bounded about the town in his favourite yellow dressing gown.

The Little Match-girl

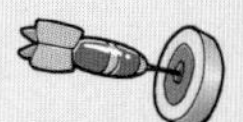

Sentence work

- To think about the best adverbs to use

Adverbs

Remember, **adverbs** tell us more about verbs.

The little girl padded quietly through the streets.

verb

adverb

The **adverb** *quietly* describes *how* the little girl *padded* through the streets.

Helpful words

swiftly quietly quickly
sweetly loudly neatly
untidily gracefully
lightly greedily hungrily
slowly speedily soundly

1 Copy each verb, and next to it write two ***ly*** adverbs that might be used to describe it. The first one is done for you.

run – quickly swiftly

talk sing write dance eat read sleep

Helpful words

slowly nervously
anxiously quickly
timidly sadly

2 Copy this sentence three times. Each time use a different adverb for the gap to describe the verb **walked**.

The little girl walked ____________ about the city streets.

Speech bubbles

1 Copy this picture in your book. Write in each speech bubble what you think might have been said.

2 Write in sentences the conversation in your picture, using speech marks.

Syllables and double letters

Words have **beats**, as music has beats.
A **syllable** is one beat in a word.
The word **snow** has only **one** beat and one syllable.
The word **little** has **two** beats and two syllables.
We say **lit - tle**.

1 Here are some words with double letters:

sorry follow cross ill happy
silly hill tell little full

a Sort them into a table, like this.

Words with one syllable	Words with two syllables
hill	little

b Add two more words to each column.

2 Write a word that rhymes with each of these words. The first is done to help you.

silly *hilly* sorry follow happy fellow cattle

Sentence work

- To use speech bubbles to show conversations

Remember

We put speech marks “ and ” around the words actually spoken.

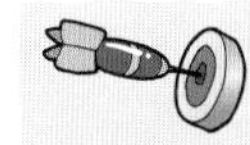

Word work

- To learn about syllables in words with double letters

Tip

Each syllable has its own vowel sound.

Helpful words

nappy lorry battle
hilly yellow hollow

Word work

- To use similar words or phrases

Definitions

Remember, a **definition** explains the *meaning* of a word.
Here are some definitions of words found in the story *The Little Match-girl*:

gloom	darkness
mottled	covered with blotches
single	one only

1 Answer these questions:

a Write a word that means the same as **two**.

b Write a word that we use for **soft, comfortable shoes worn indoors**.

c Write a word that means the same as **the place where we live**.

Helpful words

home couple
pair slippers

2 a Write your own definitions of these words:
crouched wandered bitter

b Write these phrases in your own words:
her situation was desperate
in the gathering gloom
nowhere to be found

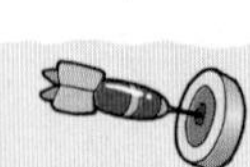

Handwriting

uppy pattern

uppy uppy uppy uppy uppy uppy uppy

1 Neatly copy the letter pattern in the box three times.

2 Make up some silly words with the uppy ending. Write a definition for each one.

Lizzy's War

Using is and was, are and were

We use **is** and **was** when we are writing about one person or thing:

Lizzy is having a drink.

We use **are** and **were** with more than one person or thing:

Lizzy's mum and Miss Lock are having a drink.

Sentence work

- To practise when to use *is*, *was*, *are* and *were*

Tip

We also use **are** and **were** with *you*.

You **are** *having a drink.*

1 Write *is* or *are* in each gap:

a *Lizzy _____ frightened by the guns.*

b *The guns _____ very noisy.*

c *Mum _____ worried that bombs might fall on their house.*

d *Miss Lock and Mum _____ sure they heard an air-raid warning.*

2 Make up an ending for each of these sentences:

a *The heavy orange curtains were __________.*

b *A bomber aircraft was __________.*

c *When the bomb hit, the people in the house were __________.*

d *Lizzy was __________.*

Sentence work

- To revise the punctuation of spoken words

Speech marks and commas

Remember, " " are called **speech marks**.
They show us the words a person said.
We usually put a comma *after* the last word actually spoken, but *before* the speech mark.
"That was an air-raid warning," said Lizzy.

1 Copy and add the missing speech marks:

Please draw the curtains, said Mum.
I have already, replied Lizzy.
Why do we need to close them? asked Lizzy.

2 Copy and add the missing speech marks and commas:

Miss Lock likes my cakes said Mum.
So do I replied Lizzy.
Don't you dare eat them all said Mum.

Word work

- To think about verbs where the vowel letters change

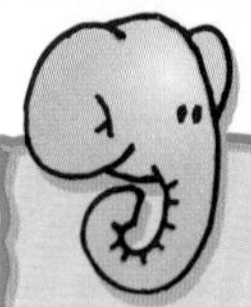

Remember

The vowel letters are ***a***, ***e***, ***i***, ***o***, ***u***.

Past and present

When writing about the past, we often add ***ed*** to verbs:

jump jump<u>ed</u>

With some verbs, we **don't** add ***ed*** when writing about what happened in the past.
Instead, we change the middle vowel letter:

s<u>i</u>t ~~sitted~~ s<u>a</u>t

1 Change the vowel letter in these words to make the past tense. The first is done for you.

sit <u>sat</u> fall sting win dig drink sing

2 Write these verbs in the present tense:

gave came woke shone stuck

Word work

- To put words starting with the same two letters into alphabetical order

Alphabetical order

If a group of words all begin with the same letter, they are put in **alphabetical order** using their **second letter**.

a b c d e f g h i j k l m n o p q r s t u v w x y z

bandage books broken

1 Put these words in alphabetical order using their second letter:

a shelf street screams smoke

b bomb bang blast burst

If a group of words all begin with the same first two letters, they are put in **alphabetical order** using their **third letter**.

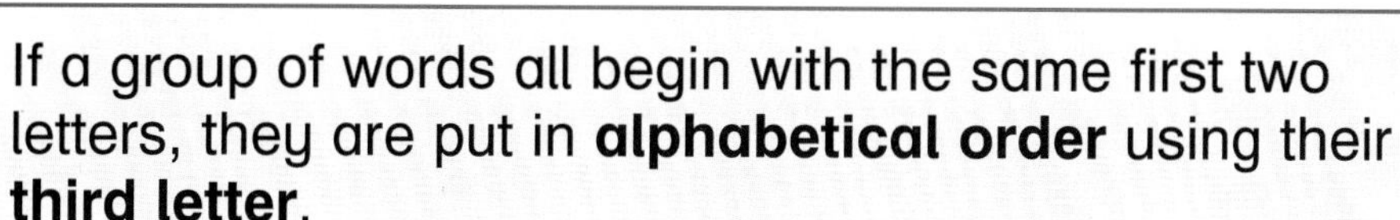

a b c d e f g h i j k l m n o p q r s t u v w x y z

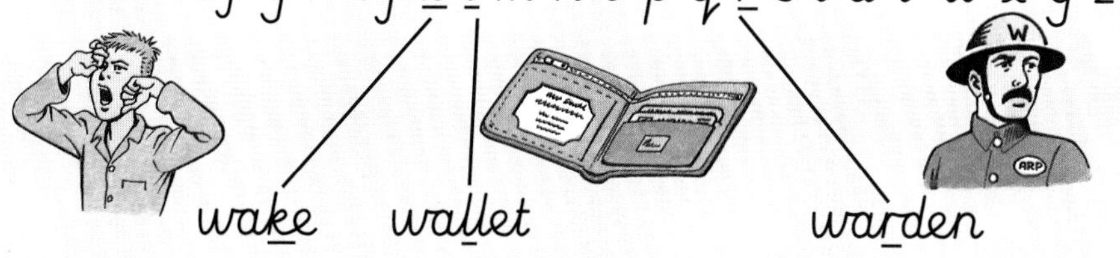

wake wallet warden

2 Put these words in alphabetical order using their third letter:

a war water wash
b bricks broken break
c shelf shake shine
d reward revive rescue

Handwriting

Practising capitals A–H

A B C D E F G H A B C D E F G H

1 Neatly copy the capital letters in the box three times.

2 Try to write a short sentence in capital letters, but you are only allowed to use these eight letters!

Build Your Own Submarine

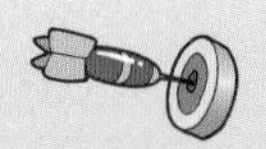

Sentence work

- To remember to write instructions in the present tense

Tip

When writing instructions, leave out personal pronouns, such as *you*, *we*, *I*.

Present tense

When we write instructions, they should be in the **present** tense, as though someone is doing it now, like this:

Fix the balloon to the tube.

Not:

You will fix the balloon to the tube.
(To be done = **future**)

You fixed the balloon to the tube.
(Has been done = **past**)

1 Copy these sentences, but write them as instructions in the present tense. The first is done for you.

a *You will need to cut a hole in the lid.*

Cut a hole in the lid.

b *Next we fixed the balloon to the tube.*

c *We passed the tube through the hole.*

d *You will need to screw the lid on tightly.*

2 Write simple, step by step instructions for a young child to follow, explaining how to make a sandwich.

Writing conversations

Sentence work

- To realise that speech can be written in different ways

Be careful or you will cut yourself.

The teacher's words can be written in different ways:

"Be careful or you will cut yourself," said Mr Desai.

Mr Desai said, "Be careful or you will cut yourself."

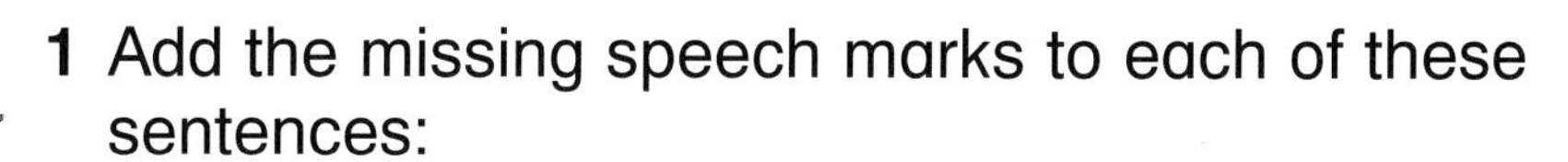

1 Add the missing speech marks to each of these sentences:

a Ann said, I'm going to paint my submarine blue.

b I'm going to paint my submarine blue, Ann said.

c Tim said, I think it would look better red.

d I think it would look better red, Tim said.

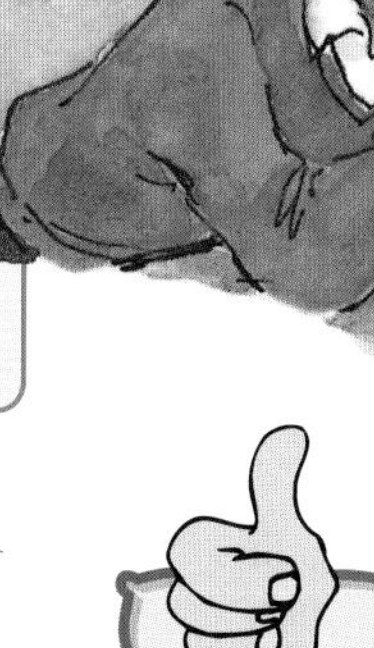

Tip

Look carefully at how the commas and full stops are used.

2 Change these sentences, so that the name of the speaker is at the beginning:

a "The paint will come off in the water," said Max.

b "It won't if we use oil paint," said Hansa.

c "Oil paint takes ages to dry," said Manjit.

d "It is worth waiting," said Hansa.

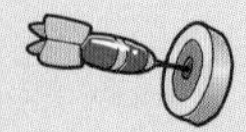

Word work

- To learn about homophones

Helpful words

won there threw to two so hear some sea no peace sew

Helpful words

heel wheel heal weave there their

Homophones

Homophones are words that sound the same but are spelt differently and have different meanings:

Fix the balloon to the end.

I have two balloons.

1 Copy these words and next to each one write a homophone. The first one is done to help you.

one won their piece through know

too sow see here sum

2 Some contractions sound like other words. Write a word that sounds like:

he'll they're we'll we've

Word work

- To revise antonyms

Opposites

Some words have the opposite meaning of another word.

Tip

An **antonym** is a word with an opposite meaning.

1 Copy these lists. Draw lines to match the opposites.

inside	weak
empty	up
long	outside
strong	full
big	short
down	small

2 Add the prefix *un* or *dis* to make these words have the opposite meaning:

happy	certain	satisfied	trust
pleased	appear	sure	well

Remember

A **prefix** is a group of letters at the beginning of a word.

dis pattern

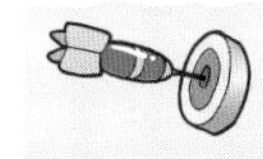

Handwriting

1 Neatly copy the letter pattern in the box three times.

2 Use a dictionary to help you find and neatly write ten words beginning with ***dis***.

Charlie and the Chocolate Factory

Sentence work

- To revise adjectives

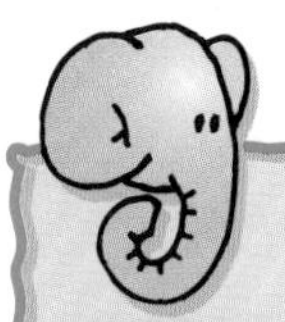

Remember

Adjectives are sometimes called **describing words**.

Adjectives

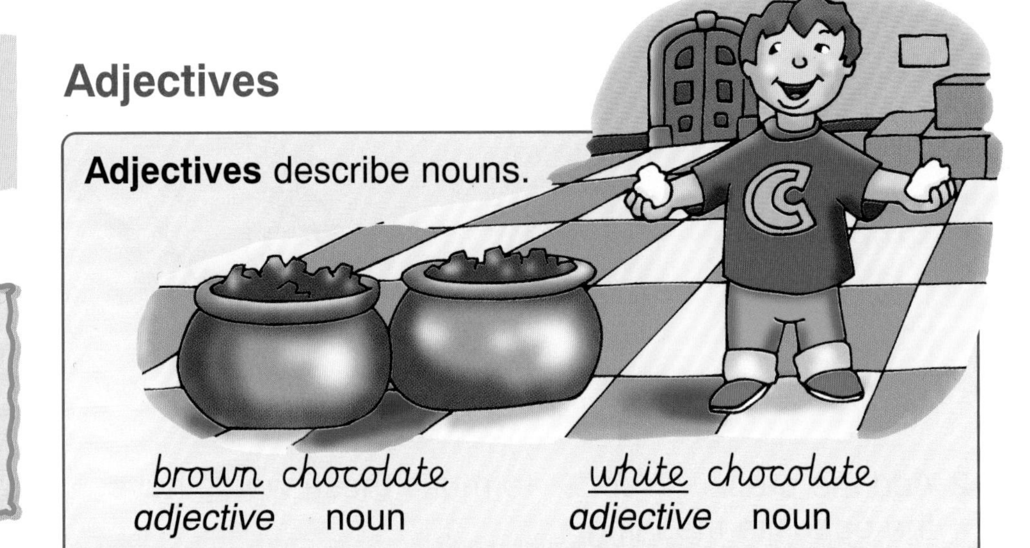

1 Write an adjective and a noun for each of these pictures. Underline the adjectives.

2 Sometimes we need to use more than one adjective to describe a noun. Copy this table and write adjectives to describe each of these nouns in the picture of Mr Wonka.

What size?	What colour?	Noun
small	red	rose
		hat
		bow-tie
		hair

Helpful words

ginger large
blue big
long red

Making words smaller

A **contraction** is made by leaving out some letters and putting an **apostrophe** (') in their place.

I'll is a contraction for **I will**.
The **apostrophe** shows where ***wi*** has been left out.

1 Write a contraction for each of these:

she is   I am   it is   would not
do not   we are   has not   there is

2 Put a contraction for the words underlined:

a Charlie <u>had not</u> seen a room like this before.
b "<u>It is</u> amazing," he thought.
c "<u>I would</u> love to work here," he said.

Sentence work

- To use apostrophes in contractions

Tip

Contract means to get smaller.
When we make a contraction, we **close the space** between the words.

Helpful words

hasn't wouldn't
it's we're
she's don't
I'm there's

Word work

- To practise the phonemes *air, are, ere, ear*

air, *are*, *ere*, *ear* words

In some words the letters ***air***, ***are***, ***ere*** and ***ear*** have a similar sound.

1 Look at the picture. Choose an ***air***, ***are***, ***ere*** or ***ear*** word to fill the gaps.

a When Charlie walked into the gigantic room, all he could do was ________ at what he saw.

b ________ were pipes all over the ceiling and walls.

c Mr Wonka stood on a ________ to look in one machine.

d Charlie wondered why they mixed ________ with the chocolate.

Helpful words

pears stair hair
where There bear
chair dare share
tear stare

2 Write four sentences about Charlie Bucket. In each sentence use a word with ***air***, ***are***, ***ere*** or ***ear***.

Word work

- To revise syllables

Syllables

In Mr Wonka's favourite room ...
kettles were hissing,
pans were sizzling,
iron machines were spluttering.

Say these words out loud.
Listen carefully to the syllables (beats) in each word.

hiss	*kettle*
hiss has **one** syllable	**kettle** has **two** syllables
(hiss)	(ket/tle)

Tip

Tap to the beats as you say the words.

1 Copy each word.
Put a line between each syllable.
Write how many syllables each word has, like this:

sizzle siz/zle two syllables

miss cabbage cotton ribbon kitten
bell common still rotten

Tip

Each syllable has one vowel sound.

2 Look in your reading book and copy five more two-syllable words.

ar, *are* and *ear* patterns

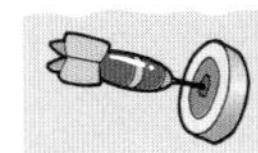

Handwriting

ar are ar ear ar are ar ear

1 Neatly copy the letter patterns in the box three times.

2 Neatly copy these words:

car bar tar jar far

care mare rare glare stare

ear dear fear gear year

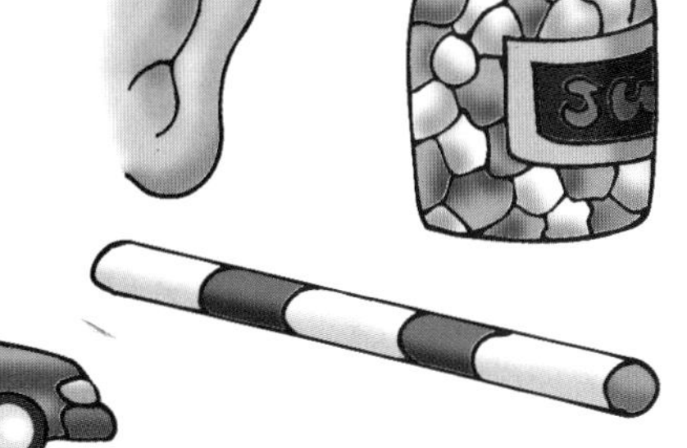

Keeping a Hamster

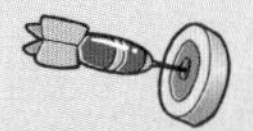

Sentence work

- To revise and extend adjectives that compare

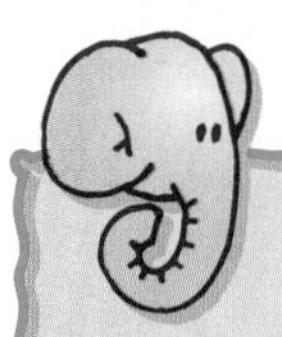

Remember

A **suffix** is a group of letters added at the end of a word.

Tip

Some short words, like *big* and *thin*, need their last letter doubled before a suffix is added.

Comparing adjectives

Remember, when we compare **two** things, we add ***er*** to an adjective. When we compare **more than two** things, we add ***est*** to an adjective.

Tom's hamster cage is bigger than Matt's.

It is the biggest of all his friend's cages.

Sometimes we add the suffix ***ish*** to a comparing word.

1 Copy and complete this table of comparing adjectives:

long	longer	longest	longish
narrow			
short			
slow			
high			
big	bigger		
thin			

2 Write a sentence that uses two adjectives which have the ***ish*** suffix.

Who owns it?

Sentence work

- To learn when to use apostrophes for ownership

When something belongs to someone we use an apostrophe (') and an ***s***, like this: ***'s***

Tim's hamster

Tim's is called a **possessive noun**.

1 Write these using possessive nouns:

a the cage belonging to the hamster

the hamster's cage

b the food belonging to the hamster

c the poster Tim made

d the computer belonging to the school

e the paints belonging to the teacher

f the rabbit belonging to Richard

2 Write each of these phrases in a sentence:

Tim's hamster

the hamster's front teeth

the teacher's finger

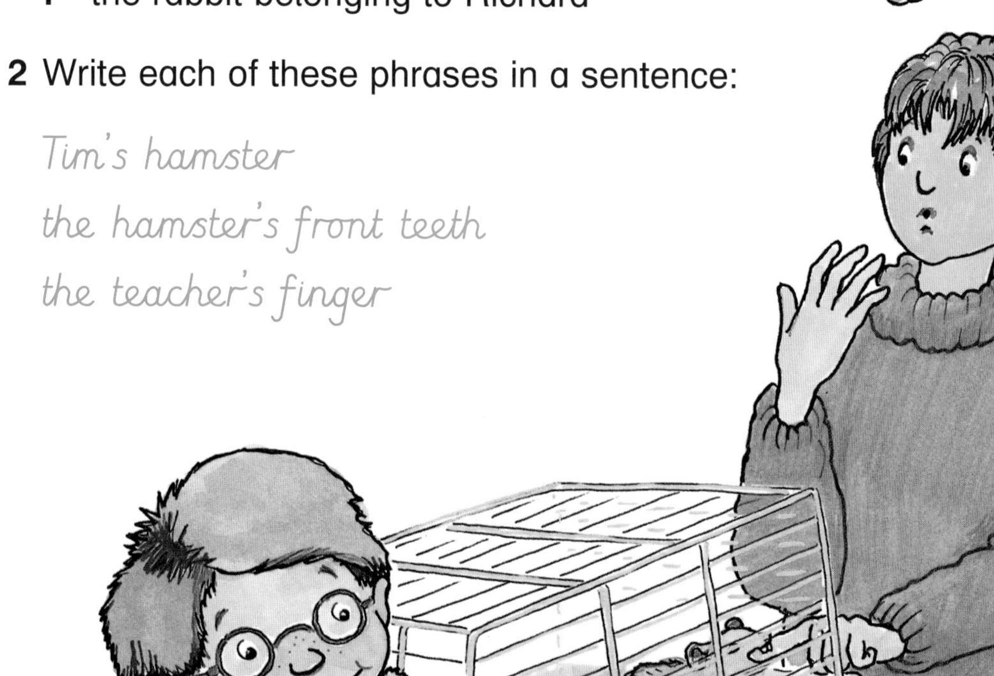

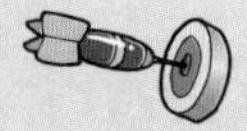

Word work

- To practise the phonemes *or*, *aw*, *ore*, and *al*

or, aw, ore, al words

In some words the letters ***or***, ***aw***, ***ore*** and ***al*** have a similar sound:

record paw sore almost

1 Neatly copy this passage about hamsters. Underline all the words that have a similar sound, like ***aw*** in **saw**.

When hamsters are born they are always very small. Even when a hamster has grown to its full size it is still small, with tiny paws, but can crawl about very quickly. It keeps its teeth sharp by gnawing and stores food in its cheeks. If a hamster was to fall from a high place it would hurt itself.

2 Write three other words for each of the four letter patterns.

Word work

- To practise putting words into alphabetical order

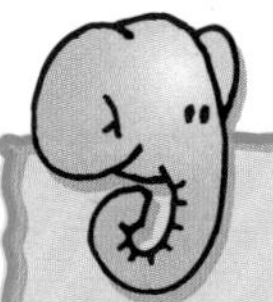

Remember

The letters in the alphabet are in **alphabetical order**.

Alphabetical order

a b c d e f g h i j k l m n o p q r s t u v w x y z

hamster horse hyena

Remember, if a group of words all begin with the same letter, they are put in **alphabetical order** using their *second letter*.

If the second letter in each word is the same, look at *the third or fourth letter.*

a b c d e f g h i j k l m n o p q r s t u v w x y z

daffodil daisy dandelion

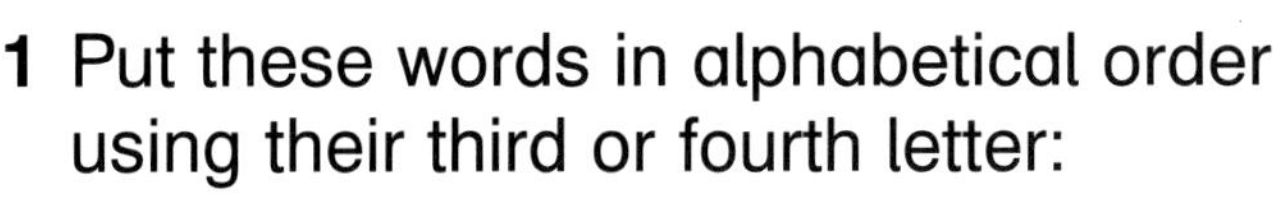

1 Put these words in alphabetical order using their third or fourth letter:

a sneeze sniff snore

b drain dragon draw

c question quarrel quiet

d trust truck trumpet

e mint mind minute

Tip

First sort the words by their first letters, and if more than one word has the same first letter, sort those words by their second, third or fourth letters.

2 Put these words in alphabetical order:

a hamster nuts hard nibble

b cage catch clean pet

c fruit greens fresh cabbage

d bush care butter burn

Handwriting

all pattern

all all all all all all all all all all all all

1 Neatly copy the letter pattern in the box three times.

2 Find and write as many words as you can with this letter pattern.

Unit 10

The Space Journey

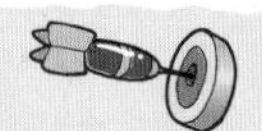

Sentence work

- To practise adding suffixes to words ending with *y*

Comparing adjectives

Remember, comparing adjectives are made by adding the suffix ***er*** or ***est***:

small   smaller   smallest

But if the adjective ends in ***y***, this must be changed to ***i*** before ***er*** or ***est*** is added:

happy   happier   happiest

1 Copy these words, and add *er* and *est* to each one. The first one is done for you.

silly sillier silliest

merry   crazy   funny   furry   sleepy
weary   jolly   pretty   dozy

2 Copy these sentences, changing the word underlined by adding the suffix it needs:

a *It was the scary monster I'd ever seen.*

b *His coat was even furry than my cat's.*

c *It had the silly tuft of hair on its head you could imagine.*

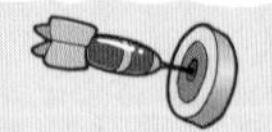

Sentence work

- To learn the rule for plural possessive nouns

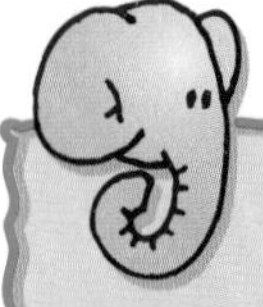

Remember

Plural means more than one.

Plural possessive nouns

Remember, when something belongs to someone we use an apostrophe (') and an ***s***, like this: ***'s***.

The boy's rucksack
(the rucksack belonging to the boy)

For plurals of nouns, like boys, we must put the apostrophe **after** the ***s***.

The three boys' rucksacks.

1 Copy each phrase, adding an apostrophe in the correct place:

a *the two girls books* b *the four creatures howls*

c *the three dogs leads* d *the five birds nests*

e *the four snakes fangs* f *the two eagles claws*

2 Write a sentence for each of these phrases that shows you know whether the possessive noun is plural or singular:

a *the trees' leaves*

b *the creature's howl*

c *the boy's anxiety*

d *the monkeys' noise*

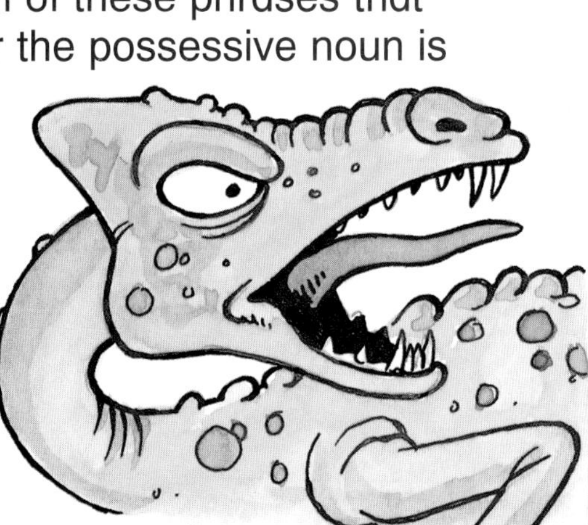

Remember

Singular means one.

ea words

Word work

- To revise *ea* words

Remember, the letters ***ea*** can have two very different sounds:

The creature was eating some leaves at the top of the tree.

With dread James slowly moved his head to look at it.

1 Copy the table. Sort the words into the correct columns.

meat bead bread seal dead beach cream thread tread

Words like head	*Words like eat*

2 Add two more words to each column.

Word work

- To use better words than good and nice

Helpful words

exciting thrilling
kind friendly
fascinating enjoyable

Choosing better words

Some words like **good** and **nice** are used too often in our writing, like this:

James is a nice boy. He has a nice time with his friends but he also has nice adventures by himself.

These words make the piece of writing much more interesting:

James is a friendly boy. He has a great time with his friends but he also has exciting adventures by himself.

1 Write these sentences. Put a more interesting word where *nice* or *good* has been used.

a *James had a good time in space.*

b *James's friends were nice to him when he returned.*

c *James wrote a nice story about his space adventure.*

d *His teacher thought his story was good.*

e *James hoped he would have another good adventure soon.*

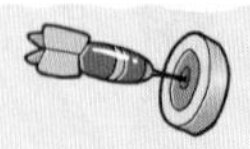

Handwriting

Practising capitals I–P

I J K L M N O P I J K L M N O P

1 Neatly copy the capital letters in the box three times.

2 Write a boy's and a girl's name that begins with each of these letters.

Whales

Using more and most

Sentence work

- To understand when more and most should be used

When we compare things we often add ***er*** or ***est*** to an adjective:

*the larg**est** sea creature*

When we use longer adjectives, it sounds odd to add ***er*** or ***est***, so instead we add **more** or **most** before the word:

A blue whale is more enormous than an elephant.

A blue whale is the most enormous creature in the world.

1 Copy each word, putting *more* and *most* in front:

beautiful *horrific* *important* *wonderful*
attractive *nervous* *frightening* *peaceful*

2 Copy this table. Fill in the missing words.

Adjective	+ er or more	+ est or most
short	shorter	
happy		happiest
ugly		
thoughtful		
nervous	more nervous	
important		

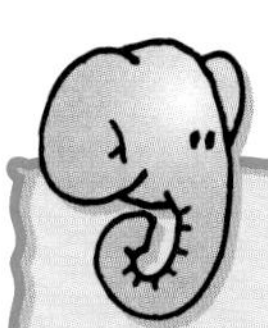

Remember

Change ***y*** to ***i*** before adding ***er*** or ***est***.

Sentence work

- To learn the rule for possessive special plural nouns

Special plurals

Remember, when something belongs to several people or animals we must put an apostrophe **after** the ***s***:

The two whales' fins were damaged.

But some plural nouns are special, and don't end in ***s***:

one child two children one man two men

For words like this, we add ***'s*** (not s'):

The children's clothes. The men's boats.

Tip

The last word in question 1 is a trick!

1 Write the plural of each of these words:

foot goose child woman
mouse tooth sheep

2 Add the missing apostrophe where it is needed:

a the childrens work **b** the mens helmets

c the mices cage **d** the womens coats

Word work

- To practise some important letter patterns

Some important word endings

Some letter patterns appear quite often in words:

light might sight right
town clown drown down
beach reach teach preach

1 Sort the words in the box below into three sets.

could train should sail would
nail brain tail strain

2 Add more words to each list, if you can.

Helpful words

main fail rain rail
pain trail plain
frail mail snail

Definitions

Word work

- To practise using a dictionary

A dictionary gives us a **definition** of a whale.

wet	*adj.* soaked in liquid, not dry	
whale	*n.* the largest sea animal. It looks like a fish.	
wharf	*n.* a landing stage to which ships can be moored	

A **definition** tells us what a word means in as few words as possible.

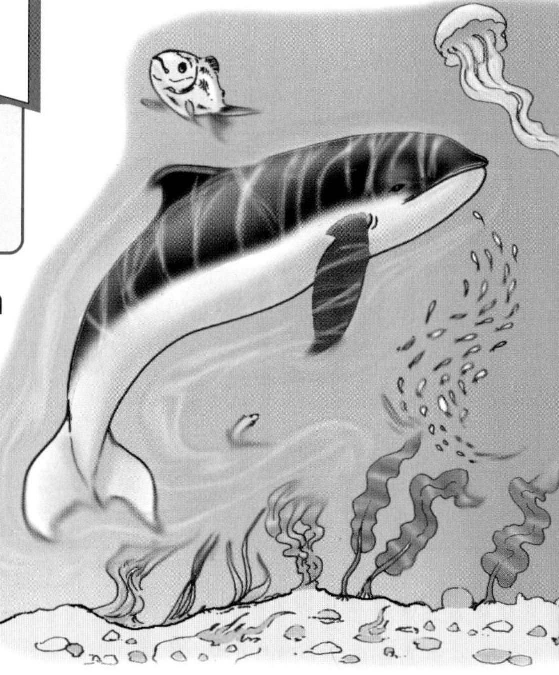

1 Use a dictionary to help you match these words with their definitions:

filter	a sea animal that looks like a small whale
porpoise	a warm-blooded animal that breathes air
creature	something that removes solids from a liquid
mammal	a living thing that moves

2 Write a short, simple definition for each of these words, like this:

milk *a white liquid*

town dinosaur elephant potato

Tip

Use a dictionary to help you.

ould pattern

Handwriting

ould ould ould ould ould ould ould

1 Neatly copy the letter pattern in the box three times.

2 Neatly copy these words twice each:

could would should

couldn't wouldn't shouldn't

The Lion, the Witch and the Wardrobe

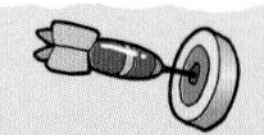

Sentence work

- To choose the best adjective for each noun

Choosing adjectives

A light breeze sprang up

The author could have said that the breeze was:

gentle light steady strong

As we write we need to think carefully about the best adjectives that describe what we want to tell our readers.

1 Make lists of adjectives that describe:

a how big or small something is

b how fast or slow something moves

c how happy or sad someone is

2 Sort these adjectives into order:

a Start with the hottest: chilly warm hot cold

b Start with the easiest: difficult easy impossible

c Start with the most gentle: wild tame gentle vicious

d Start with the biggest: tiny large massive small

fast massive chirpy small jolly express speedy large rapid quick unhappy merry joyful downcast tiny slow depressed huge minuscule sluggish

Using apostrophes

Sentence work

- To practise using apostrophes

Remember, we use apostrophes in contractions:

I'm you'll wouldn't

and we use apostrophes to show who owns or has something:

the girl's coat the two boys' bags

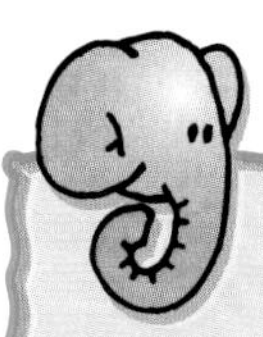

Remember

In contractions, the apostrophe is put where the letters have been left out.

1 Make a table, like this.

Contractions	Possessive nouns

Sort these phrases into the two columns:

the professor's house the girls' room
can't see she's hungry
the wardrobe's mirror the goat's legs
I'm amazed he wouldn't come

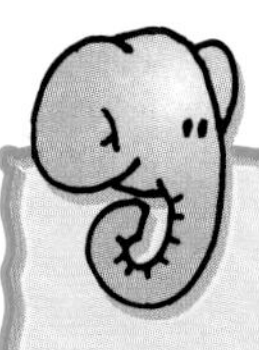

Remember

Possessive nouns show who owns or has something.

2 Write a sentence that includes at least one contraction and one possessive noun.

The prefix and suffix *al*

Word work

- To practise the *al* pattern as a prefix and suffix

This magical scene is from the book The Lion, the Witch and the Wardrobe.

The mist turned from white to gold and presently cleared away altogether.

Tip

All right is always two words – *not* one!

1 Add the prefix or suffix *al* to make a word:

music most so medic sign though ways comic

2 Make a funny or nonsense sentence that includes all of these words:

altogether always accidental comical

Word work

- To revise and spot mistakes when using some common prefixes and suffixes

Misspelt words

When we write we sometimes make mistakes in our spelling of words.
It is always important to check our work to see if we can spot the mistakes we make.
In past units you have learnt about the prefixes ***un***, ***dis***, ***mis*** and ***al*** and the suffixes ***ful***, ***ness*** and ***al***.

1 Spot the words below which are spelt incorrectly.
Copy the words that are spelt correctly.
Write the correct spellings for the other words.

goodness allways allmost unnsure
illness helpfull alltogether equal
miscount unndress allso beautifull

2 a Write two words that begin with each of these prefixes: *un*, *dis*, *mis*, *al*.

b Write two words that end with each of these suffixes: *ful*, *ness*, *al*.

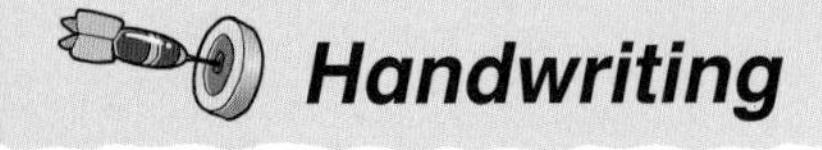

Handwriting

Practising capitals Q–Z

Q R S T U V W X Y Z

1 Neatly copy the capital letters in the box three times each.

2 Write your name in capital letters.

Looking at Trees

Adjective phrases

Sometimes a single adjective is all we need to describe a noun:

An old tree stands next to the school.

Our readers get more information if we write:

An old tree covered with red, juicy apples stands next to the school.

old is a single **adjective**.
covered with red, juicy apples is an **adjective phrase**.

Sentence work

- To introduce adjective phrases

1 Copy these sentences and neatly underline the adjective phrase in each one. Put a circle around the noun that is being described.

  a *The pictures, colourful and well drawn, made a good display.*

  b *Mr Green, normally a quiet and gentle man, became very cross when he saw the men chopping down the trees.*

  c *The forest, dark and spooky and very quiet, made me shiver slightly.*

  d *Three trees, each tall and elegant, grew by the lake.*

2 Use these adjective phrases in sentences of your own:

  a *smooth with crinkled edges*

  b *swaying and bending in the wind*

  c *interesting, colourful and neatly set out*

Tip

A group of words is called a **phrase**.

Sentence work

- To learn about the importance of the order of words in sentences

Word order

The order in which words are written is important.

The man fell off the tree who was picking apples. ✗

The man who was picking apples fell off the tree. ✓

1 Copy these sentences, but write the words in a different order so that it changes the meaning:

a *The man climbed the old tree with long legs.*

b *The girl planted the flowers in red dungarees.*

2 Write a sentence to explain the difference in meaning between these sentences:

a We must finish the bark rubbing before we can go.
We must go before we can finish the bark rubbing.

b I will only do leaf printing if you help me.
I will do leaf printing if only you help me.

Words ending in *ind* and *ild*

Word work

- To practise some common word endings

"To do a bark rubbing first you need to **find** a tree!" laughed the ch**ild**.

1 Look at the picture on page 44. Match each number with one of these words:

wild *unwind* *behind* *child* *unkind*

2 **Wind** can have two different sounds and two different meanings. Write a sentence using each of the meanings.

Plurals

To make a noun ending in ***f*** plural, **drop the *f*** and add ***ves***:

1 Change these nouns into their plural form:

2 Copy these sentences, adding *ing* to the words underlined:

a *We need more shelf in our classroom.*

b *The cow mooed loudly as it was calf.*

ve pattern

ve ve ve ve ve ve ve ve ve ve ve ve ve

1 Neatly copy the letter pattern in the box three times.

2 a Neatly copy again the plurals you have made that end with *ves*.

b Use a dictionary to help you write ten words that begin with *ve*.

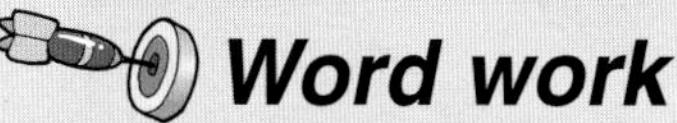

Word work

- To learn how nouns ending with *f* are made into plurals

Remember

Plural means more than one.

Tip

To add ***ing***, think how you added ***s***.

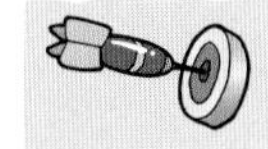

Handwriting

Cows

Sentence work

- To use *is* and *are* correctly in sentences

Using is and are

In the *Cows* poem by James Reeves the brown cow says, 'Flies is very tiresome', which is wrong.

It can be difficult to remember when to use **am**, **is** and **are**. We use **is** with one person or thing:

"The fly is very tiresome," said the brown cow.

We use **are** with more than one person or thing:

"Flies are very tiresome," said the brown cow.

1 Why should the brown cow have said, 'Flies **are** very tiresome.'?

2 Write *is* or *are* in each gap:

a The cows ___ coming in for milking.

b The farmer's daughter ___ fetching them.

c They ___ walking slowly.

d The farmer ___ getting the milking parlour ready.

e Every day the farmer and his daughter ___ up by five o'clock to do the milking.

Sentence work

- To practise when and how to join sentences

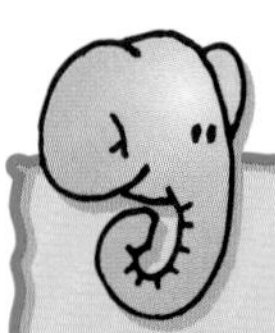

Remember

Conjunctions are sometimes called joining words.

Using conjunctions

Remember, **conjunctions** help us to write longer, more interesting sentences.

The cows were pleased to return to the field by the stream. They like the grass in that field.

The cows were pleased to return to the field by the stream because they like the grass there.

because is a conjunction in this sentence.

1 Join each of these pairs of sentences:

a The cows were milked by three o'clock. The milk tanker didn't collect the milk until six o'clock.

b The family worked very hard to run the farm. They all agreed they wouldn't want to do anything else.

2 Write the conjunction in each of these sentences:

a The cows were sitting down and relaxing when a swarm of flies started biting them.

b The children work with their father every evening though when they leave school they hope to work on the farm full-time.

Helpful words

and but so because although though after for until yet then as or when while so

Root words

Word work

- To learn about root words

Many words are built by adding prefixes and suffixes to shorter (root) words:

kindness (root: kind, suffix: ness) unkind (prefix: un, root: kind)

Thinking about root words can help make long words easier to spell:

unkindness (prefix: un, root: kind, suffix: ness)

1 Copy these words and next to each write the root word. The first one is done for you.

munched munch chewing unsure working helpful children untidy disliked magical

Helpful words

like tidy help magic chew munch child work sure

2 Sometimes a root word is slightly changed when suffixes are added. Write the root word next to each of these words. The first one is done for you.

flies fly tasty coming laziness squabbling prettiest heavier foggy

Helpful words

fog heavy pretty fly lazy taste come squabble

Word work

- To learn about gender words

Tip

Words that tell us whether a person or animal is male or female are called **gender words**.

Tip

Words with the suffix ***ess*** are usually **feminine**.

Helpful words

actress stewardess
lioness hostess
waitress princess

Gender words

Some words are only used for **females**.
They are **feminine** words:

cow

Some words are only used for **males**.
They are **masculine** words:

bull

1 Sort the words into their correct gender column.

lord bull boy woman bridegroom
brother queen prince girl lady
cow man bride sister king princess

Masculine	Feminine
boy	girl

2 Copy these words. Next to each, write the opposite gender. The first one is done for you. Check your spellings in a dictionary.

actor <u>actress</u> waiter steward host lion prince

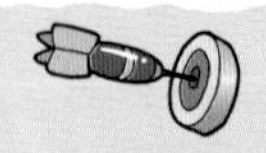

Handwriting

ess pattern

ess ess ess ess ess ess ess ess ess ess ess

1 Neatly copy the letter pattern in the box three times.

2 a Write a word that has *ess* as part of it, beginning with:

cr dr gu l m pr

b Write three feminine words that end with *ess*

In the Playground

Changing verbs

Sentence work

- To discover some ways verbs can be changed

Remember, words like **kicked** tell us what action is taking place.
Verbs can be put into *families*.
Verb family names start with **to**.

Family name	Verbs in the family
to kick	kick kicks kicking kicked
to play	play plays playing played

1 Make a table, like the one above, and write in it the details of these verb families:

to hate to turn to smile to kiss to punch

2 Add these to your table, but be careful:

to see to think to throw to blow to fall

Tip

Some verb families are tricky!

Helpful words

saw fell blew
thought threw

Sentence work

- To practise how to lay out letters

Remember

The beginning of a letter needs:

1 Your address, so the person can write back.
2 The date, so they know when you wrote the letter.
3 The name of the person you are writing to.

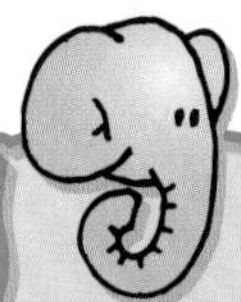

Remember

The end of a letter needs:

1 A friendly last sentence
2 A signing-off phrase
3 Your name, so the reader knows who wrote the letter.

Writing letters

Blaxland Primary School
Penrith Road
Blaxland
BD4 5SL

16th May

Dear Jessica,

I had a brilliant idea today. I thought you would find it funny, so I'm writing to tell you about it.

There is a boy at school who keeps calling me names and kicking me. I suddenly thought that the thing he would hate most in all the world would be a big kiss. So I gave him one!

I was right. He hated being kissed. He was so surprised he hardly moved, so I punched him on the nose. I know I shouldn't have done, but he has been so unkind to me I couldn't stop myself! All my friends laughed, but my teacher was cross – well just a bit!

I look forward to seeing you soon.

With best wishes,

Ann

1 Set out the top of a letter, using the address of your school, or your home address.

2 Write the ending for a letter, as if you had written to an aunt who lives in another country.

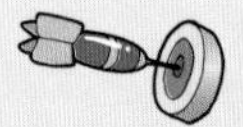

Word work

- To practise words with the *wa* letter pattern

wa words

1 Write five words that begin with ***wa***.

2 Copy the sentences. Fill in the gaps with *wa* words.

a *The young children _____ to go near the _____ but it was too dangerous.*

b *The ____ floated down the river in the ____ sun.*

c *_____ out for the _____, it might sting you.*

d *Misha _____ pleased to have a _____ after falling in the muddy _____.*

Helpful words

swan wanted swamp
wasp water warm
wash watch was

Compound words

When two small words are put together to make one bigger word, it is called a **compound word**.

playground is made from *play* and *ground*

Word work

- To make compound words

1 Copy these two lists and draw lines to connect words that can make compound words. Then write the compound words you have discovered.

with	*board*	
cup	*out*	*without*
in	*room*	
bath	*side*	

2 Write as many compound words as you can that begin with: *play every some*

wh and *wa* patterns

wh wa wh wa wh wa wh wa wh wa

Handwriting

1 Neatly copy the letter patterns in the box three times.

2 Neatly copy this silly sentence:

Why was the white swan washing while wasps were swimming in the warm, swampy water?

Hue Boy

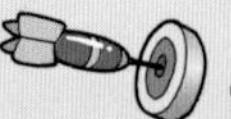

Sentence work

- To learn about adverbs

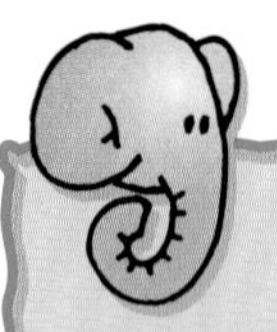

Remember

Adjectives tell us more about people, places and things.

Adverbs tell us more about actions.

Tip

Change the ***y*** to ***i*** before adding ***er*** or ***est***.

Comparing words

Adjectives describe nouns. We often add ***er*** or ***est*** to adjectives if we want to compare nouns:

Hue Boy was the smallest boy.

comparing adjective (smallest) — *noun* (boy)

Adverbs describe verbs. We can also add ***er*** or ***est*** to adverbs to compare verbs:

Hue Boy could run faster than the others.

verb (run) — *comparing adverb* (faster)

1 Copy and finish this table.

run quickly	run quicker	run quickest
walk slowly		
jump high		

2 Write two comparing adverbs that can be made from these: *guilty* *silly* *funny* *weary*

Sentence work

- To learn how speech can be written in different ways

Writing conversations

Mum's words below can be written in three different ways, depending on whether **cried Mum** is at the end, the beginning or in the middle:

"Lawdy. This problem seems to be bigger than this village!" cried Mum.

Mum cried, "Lawdy. This problem seems to be bigger than this village!"

"Lawdy," cried Mum. "This problem seems to be bigger than this village!"

1 Look carefully at the sentences in the box on page 52. Add the missing speech marks to each of these sentences:

a *Miss Harper said, Walk tall, Hue Boy. That's all you need to do.*

b *Walk tall, Hue Boy, said Miss Harper. That's all you need to do.*

c *Walk tall, Hue Boy. That's all you need to do, said Miss Harper.*

2 Change these sentences, so that the name of the speaker is in the middle:

a *Carlos said, "I know, Hue Boy. Some stretching exercises will do the trick."*

b *"Ten minutes a day. That's all you need to do," Carlos added.*

c *His teacher said, "Stuff and nonsense! Walk tall, Hue Boy."*

Same letters, different sounds

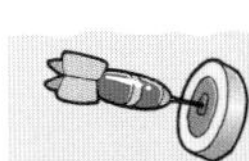

Word work

- To understand that letter groups don't always make the same sounds

Hue Boy looked d<u>ow</u>n.

Still he didn't gr<u>ow</u>.

down and gr**ow** have the same letter string (***ow***) but it makes a different sound in the two words.

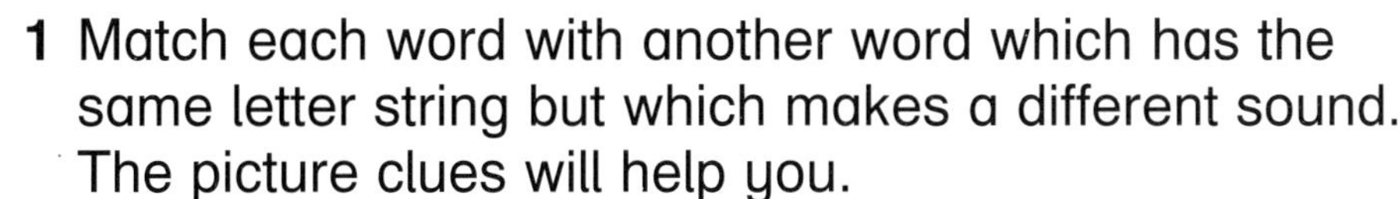

1 Match each word with another word which has the same letter string but which makes a different sound. The picture clues will help you.

lost shoot have fear height bull

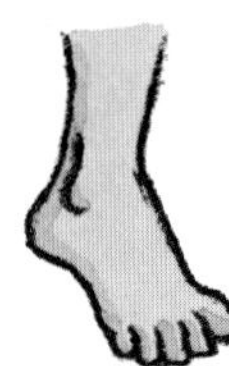
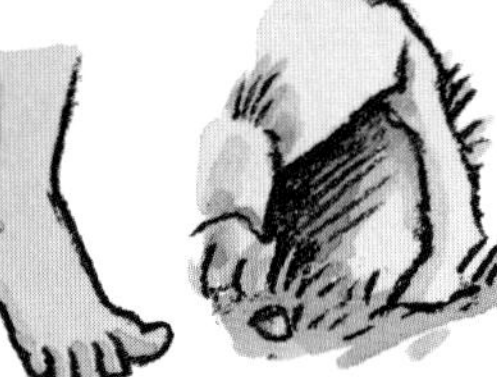

Helpful words

post gull bear eight cave foot

2 For each pair of words in question 1, write another pair yourself that rhyme with the words in the first pair. Like this:

lost post   cost most

Word work

- To learn about diminutives, and how they are made

Remember

Diminutives are sometimes formed by adding a *suffix* to a word.

Helpful words

gosling puppy kid kitten calf foal

Helpful words

owlet cygnet piglet

Diminutives

A **diminutive** is the word used for a small version of something:

duck   duckling

1 Copy these words. Write the young of each animal.

a *cat*   **b** *goat*  **c** *dog* 

d *horse*  **e** *cow*  **f** *goose* 

2 **a** Write the diminutives of these animals. They each end with ***et***.

owl   *pig*  *swan* 

b Write each of these diminutive words in a sentence:

sapling   dwarf

Handwriting

Practising capitals without curves

A E F H I K L M N T V W X Y Z

1 Neatly copy the capital letters in the box three times each. None of them has a curve.

2 Write five words in capital letters, using only the letters without curves.

The New Car Park

Adding *y* to make describing words

Adjectives and adverbs are sometimes made by adding the letter ***y*** to nouns and verbs:

I know the grassy play area looks scruffy and muddy.

grass + ***y*** = grassy
noun *adjective*

In some short words we need to double the last letter before adding ***y***:

mu**d** + ***y*** = mu**dd**y

In *magic e* words, drop the ***e*** before adding the ***y***:

slime + ***y*** = slimy

Sentence work

- To learn that describing words can be made from nouns and verbs

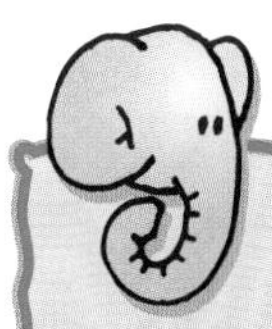

Remember

Adjectives and **adverbs** are usually describing words. **Nouns** are name words and **verbs** are action words.

1 Make adjectives from these nouns and verbs:

jump snow frost mist sand

run slop bag grime flap

Tip

Double the last letter before adding ***y*** if the letter before the last is a single vowel.

2 Copy these sentences, making adjectives or adverbs from the words underlined to fill the gaps:

a *It was a hot day, and she was feeling <u>sleep</u>.*

b *"You look very <u>dream</u>," said her dad.*

c *"The council might be <u>sneak</u>, and build the car park while we're at school," said Jessica.*

Changing sentences to make questions

Sentence work

- To discover how word order can be changed to turn statements into questions

Remember, word order in sentences is important.

Our councillor will help us.
Will our councillor help us?

By changing the order of the words, and adding a question mark, statements can be turned into questions.

1 Change these statements into questions:

a I can help you.

b We are going to write to the council.

c They are going to make a car park on our playground.

2 Write the questions that these statements answer. The first is done for you.

a Jessica wrote to Mrs Barnard.
Who did Jessica write to?

b She wrote her letter on 12th November.

c Jessica wanted Mrs Barnard to stop the car park being built.

d The council were planning to build a car park on the play area.

Helpful words

Who When
Why Where

Word work

- To practise spelling double-letter words and begin to notice some rules

Words with double letters

Jessica wrote a letter to the council because she felt cross.

1 Copy the table.
Write five words with **double letters** at the end of a word and five words with **double letters** in the middle.

Double letters at the end	Double letters in the middle
cross	letter

Tip

Here are some double letters often used in words:

ll ff ss tt bb rr

2 a How many more words can you find with ***ss***? Make a list.

b Make a list of the words you can think of that end with ***bb***, ***tt*** or ***rr***. What do you notice?

it's or its?

it's can be used instead of **it is** or **it has**:

The Green is only small, but it's the only place we have to play.

its is used when something **belongs to** something:

Do you like its colour?

1 Copy the sentences and fill each gap with *it's* or *its*:

a *"Wake-up, __ a lovely day," said Mum, "__ time we took Monty for a walk."*

b *The dog pulled at __ lead.*

c *"__ great being on holiday," said Natalie, "but __ a shame the council are building a car park on the Green."*

d *"The council can do what it likes on __ land," said Mum.*

e *Natalie had an idea, "__ time I wrote a letter!"*

2 Write a sentence that has both **its** and **it's** in it.

ll, *ff*, *tt* and *bb* patterns

ll ff tt bb ll ff tt bb ll ff tt bb ll ff tt bb

1 Neatly copy the letter patterns in the box three times.

2 Neatly copy these words. Add three more words of your own for each of these double-letter patterns.

hilly fluff little rubbish

Word work

- To learn when *its* needs an apostrophe

Remember

The apostrophe shows where letters have been left out.

Handwriting

Unit 18

Mary and Sarah

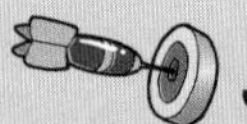

Sentence work

- To practise the main ways of making nouns plural

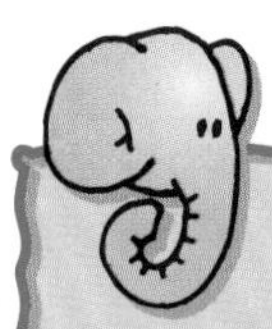

Remember

Singular means one; **plural** means more than one.

Tip

If a word is made plural by adding ***s***, ***es*** or ***ies*** it must be a noun.

Sentence work

- To discover how word order can be changed to turn questions into statements

Making plural nouns

Remember, most nouns are changed from singular to plural by adding ***s***:

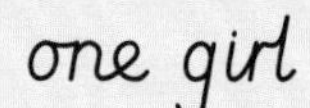

one girl *two girls*

Nouns ending with ***sh***, ***ch***, ***ss*** or ***x*** are made plural by adding ***es***:

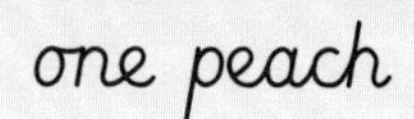

one peach *two peaches*

Most nouns ending in ***y*** are made plural by changing the ***y*** to ***i*** and adding ***es***:

one cherry *two cherries*

If a word ends in ***ay*** or ***oy***, just add ***s***.

one boy *two boys*

1 Write the plural of each of these nouns:

bristle thistle seal eel hedgehog tray

peach brush fox nappy berry toy

2 Look at these words. Copy the nouns, and then write the plural. The first is done for you.

field fields lorry sleek tune watch

all tree church with box fish

Changing sentences to make questions

Remember, word order in sentences is important.

Does Mary like smooth things?

Mary does like smooth things.

By changing the order of the words, and changing one or two of the words, questions can be turned into statements.

1 Change these questions into statements:

a *Does Sarah like rough things?*

b *Does Sarah like boats with barnacled bottoms?*

c *Does Mary like milk and silk?*

Tip

You will also need to change some of the **punctuation marks**.

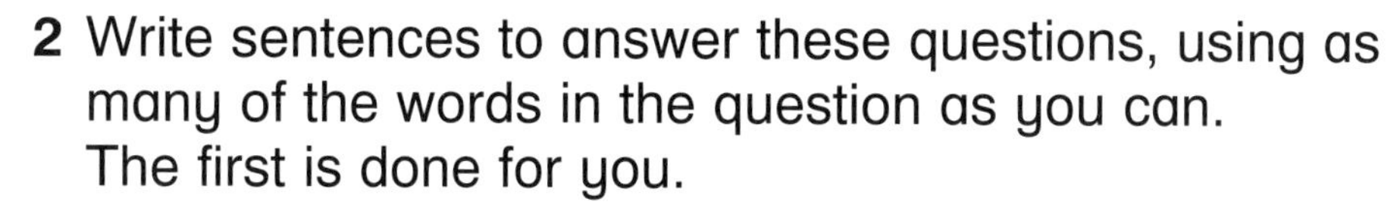

2 Write sentences to answer these questions, using as many of the words in the question as you can. The first is done for you.

a *Is polish rough or smooth?*
Polish is smooth.

b *Do barnacles stick to the bottom of boats?*

c *Are hedgehogs' spines rough or smooth?*

Same letters, different sounds

Word work

- To find how letter patterns don't always make the same sounds

Rough and **plough** have the same letter string (***ough***) but it makes a different sound in each of the two words.

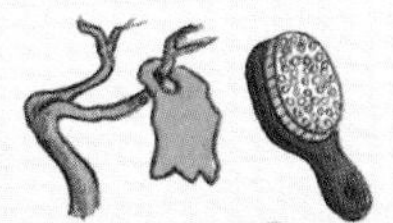
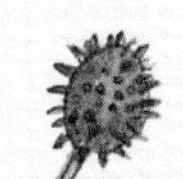
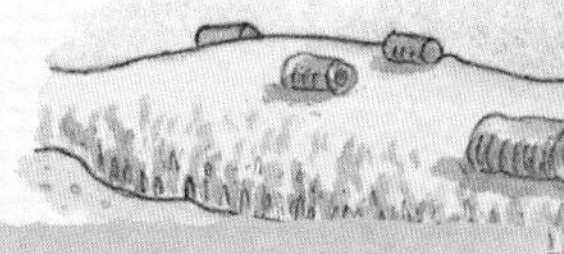
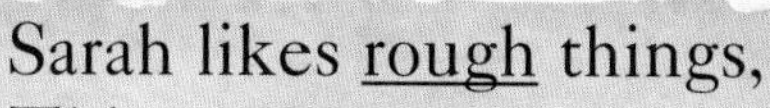

Sarah likes rough things,
Things all troubly:
Crags, snags, bristles, thistles, fields left stubbly.

1 Match each word with another word which has the same letter string but which makes a different sound. The picture clues will help you.

snow *boot* *move* *wear* *bead* *pull*

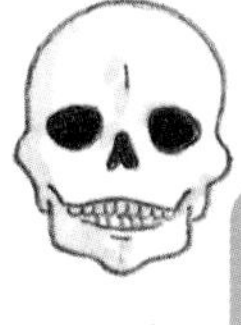

Helpful words

skull *cow* *glove*
book *ear* *head*

2 For each pair of words in question 1, write another pair yourself that rhyme with the words in the first pair. Like this: *snow cow* *blow how*

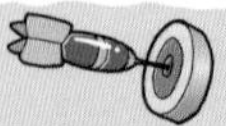

Word work

- To discover that compound words can help spelling

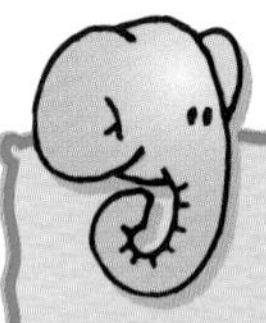

Remember

When two small words are put together to make one big word, it is called a **compound word**.

Compound words

Mary likes smooth things,
Things that glide:
Sleek skis swishing down a mountainside.

It helps, when spelling, to split a compound word into its two smaller parts, like this:

mountainside = mountain + side

1 Choose three of these compound words.
Draw a picture for each small word, like this:

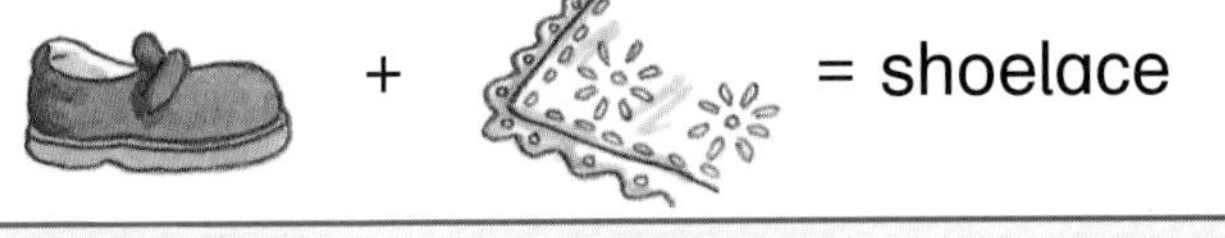
= shoelace

raindrop	*sunlight*	*snowflake*
shoelace	*handbag*	*cupboard*
keyhole	*peanut*	*earthworm*

Show your pictures to someone and see if they can work out which compound words you have drawn.

2 Look through a reading book. Make a list of ten more compound words.

Handwriting

ough pattern

ough ough ough ough ough ough

1 Neatly copy the letter pattern in the box three times.

2 a Neatly copy these words twice each:

though through plough rough tough cough

b Write a sentence that includes as many of the words as you can.

Badgers

Making plural verbs

Sentence work

- To realise that plural forms of verbs are different from plural forms of nouns

Remember, most nouns are changed from singular to plural by adding ***s*** or ***es***:

two badgers *two foxes*

But, to make verbs plural, we **remove** the final ***s*** or ***es***!

one badger digs *two badgers dig*

singular verb *plural verb*

Remember

Singular means one; **plural** means more than one.

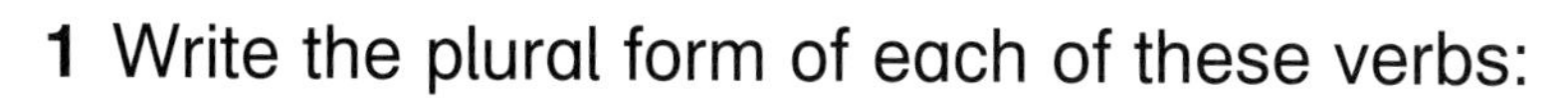

1 Write the plural form of each of these verbs:

runs sings walks speaks

throws washes rushes wishes

2 Write these sentences again, but change them from singular to plural. The first is done for you.

a A badger makes a den.
The badgers make a den.

b An owl watches from a tree.

c It eats small animals.

d The cow catches TB.

Practising punctuation

Sentence work

- To practise end-sentence punctuation

Remember, all sentences must end with a full stop, a question mark or an exclamation mark.

There is a badger.

Where is the badger?

That badger just bit me!

Tip

A full stop is at the bottom of every question mark and exclamation mark.

1 Copy these sentences. Add the missing punctuation marks.

a Do badgers come out at night

b I like to watch badgers

c Stop throwing stones or you'll hurt them

d Have you ever seen a badger

e Badgers have strong legs with large claws

2 In this passage the punctuation and capital letters are missing. Write it correctly.

it was a dark night when jennie and tim went with mrs cox to watch the badgers they went to a little wood near alcombe in somerset

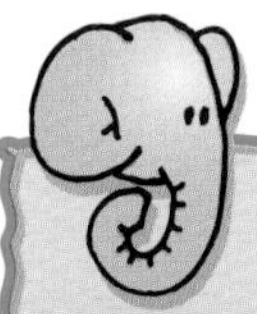

Remember

Proper nouns (names) start with a capital letter.

Word work

- To learn how root words can help with spelling

Root words

Remember, a **root word** is a word that *prefixes and suffixes* are added to, to make another word:

covered uncover covering

discover discovered

root word = cover

Tip

Some common prefixes

un dis mis de re al

Some common suffixes

ly ful ed ing est er al ment ness

1 Copy the word pairs.
Underline the root word in each word.

signal signing

revisit visited

punished punishment

helper unhelpful

disobey obeyed

repaid payment

2 Write two new words by adding prefixes or suffixes to each of these root words:

quick spell like weak suggest

Words from other languages

Look at the badgers in this photograph.

Most words that have ***ph*** in them, like *phone*, *photo*, *graph* and *sphere*, come from the Greek language.

1 Sort these words into three lists according to their Greek root word:

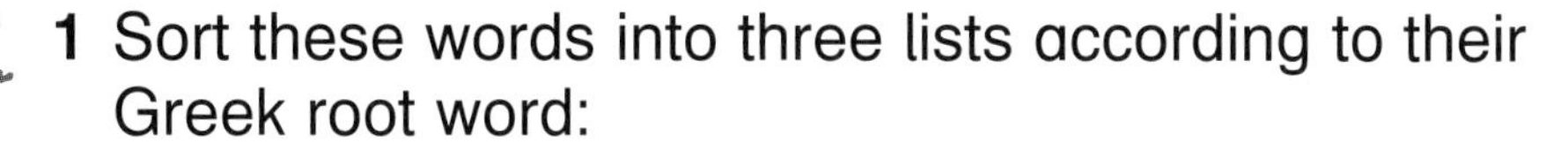

telegraph saxophone paragraph
hemisphere graph telephone atmosphere
microphone sphere autograph

2 Write a short definition of three of the words.

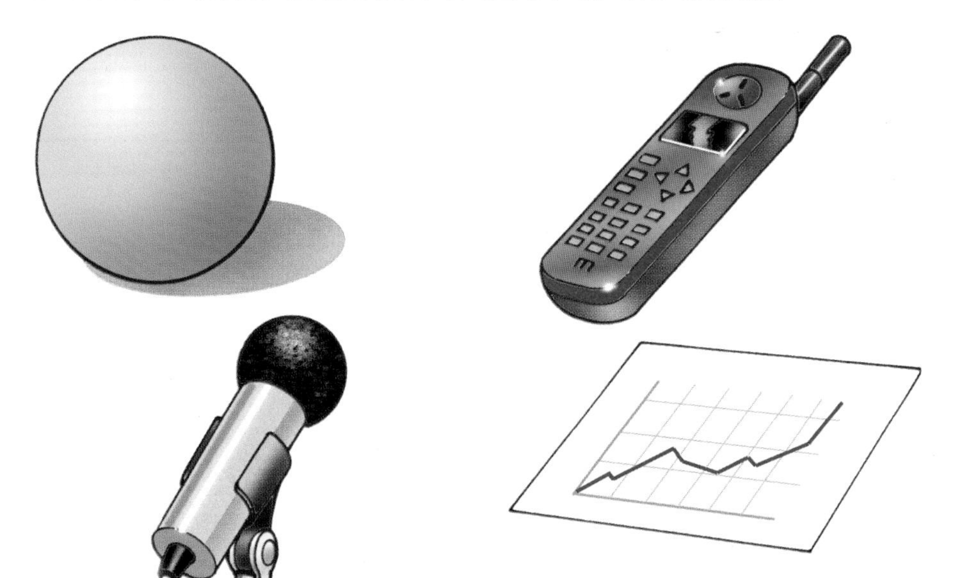

ment pattern

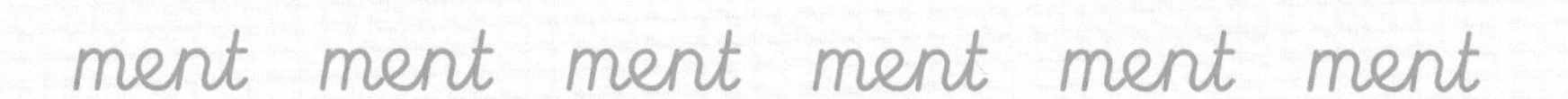
ment ment ment ment ment ment

1 Neatly copy the letter pattern in the box three times.

2 Neatly copy these words, adding the suffix *ment* to each one. Like this:

improve improvement

agree enjoy treat pay state punish base

Word work

- To introduce some Greek roots, prefixes and suffixes

Tip

In Greek:
phone means *sound*
graph means *writing*
sphere means *ball*

Handwriting

Jack and the Meanstalk

Sentence work

- To revise some of the features of nouns and verbs

Tip

If a verb has ***ed*** the action happened in the past, and if it has ***ing*** it is usually happening in the present.

Nouns or verbs?

Nouns are naming words and **verbs** are usually action words:

The plane soared up into the sky.

noun verb noun

We have found that nouns often make plurals by adding ***s*** or ***es***:

plane planes sky skies

Verbs can change, too, by having suffixes added, like ***ed*** or ***ing***, to show when the action happened:

soar soared soaring

1 Sort these words into the correct column:

television working planes plants
climbing arrived villagers soared
roof leaves jumped seeing

Nouns	Verbs

2 a Copy this sentence. Neatly underline the nouns and action verbs.

The plant grew so high that it burst through the ozone layer.

b Copy a sentence from your reading book and underline the nouns and action verbs.

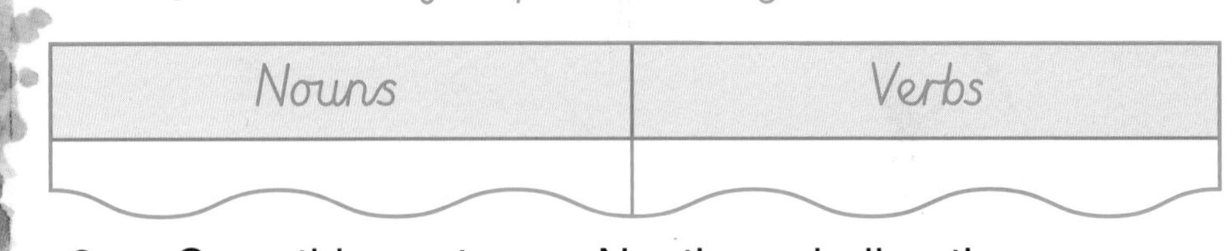

Sentence work

- To understand how sentences can be changed from positive to negative

Making negative sentences

Being **negative** is saying **no**, or saying something cannot be done:

The fighter planes couldn't shoot it down.

Being **positive** is saying **yes**, or saying something can be done:

The fighter planes could shoot it down.

1 Make these sentences negative:

a *Professor Jack liked to experiment.*

b *He had been working with plants.*

c *The giant plant was on television.*

Helpful words

hadn't wasn't didn't

2 Sort these **negative** words into two lists. In one list put the words that have apostrophes and in the other words without apostrophes.

nothing can't won't wouldn't never
no shouldn't not haven't couldn't
shan't none didn't don't

Word work

- To practise *ion* words

Suffix – *ion*

Many words end in ***sion*** or ***tion***: *Professor Jack's invention made seeds grow faster.*

The suffix ***ion*** often makes the ***shun*** sound at the end of a word: *invent + ion = invention*

1 Copy the table.
Sort these ***ion*** words into the correct group.

impression subtraction instruction
expression infection confession

Discussion	*Invention*

Remember

A **suffix** is added to the end of a word to make a new word.

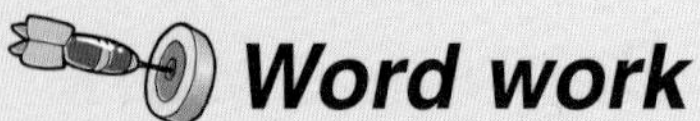

- To spot new words

New words

The words below are used in *Jack and the Meanstalk.* They would not have been used in a story 100 years ago because **television** and **fighter planes** hadn't been invented.

television crew

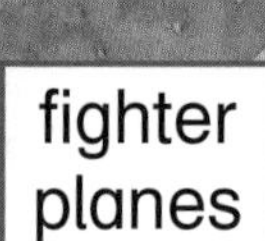

1 Copy the words you think have only been used in the last 100 years:

computer sun radio
water spaceship goat
sack hovercraft cinema
caravan valley market

2 Think of three more **new** words.

ion pattern

1 Neatly copy the letter pattern in the box three times.

2 Neatly copy these words, adding the suffix ***ion*** to each one. Like this:

discuss discussion

percuss concuss impress progress express

act attract extract subtract connect object

Opening Soon!

Adverb phrases

Sometimes a single adverb is all we need to describe a verb:

The new sports centre is opening soon.
verb adverb

Our readers get more information if we write:

The new sports centre is opening with a big party and fireworks.

The adverb phrase *with a big party and fireworks* tells us **how** the sports centre is opening.

The adverb phrase *on Saturday at 3 o'clock* tells us **when** the sports centre is opening:

The new sports centre is opening on Saturday at 3 o'clock.

The adverb phrase *where the bus garage used to be* tells us **where** the sports centre is opening:

The new sports centre is opening where the bus garage used to be.

1 Copy these sentences and neatly underline the adverb phrase in each one. Put a circle around the verb that is being described.

a *The fireworks exploded with loud bangs and colourful flashes.*

b *Dad said we can swim on Sunday morning.*

c *We parked in the car park near the shops.*

2 Use these adverb phrases in your own sentences about someone going for swimming lessons:

a *at least twice a week*

b *in the shallow end of the pool*

c *slowly and nervously*

Sentence work

- To learn about adverb phrases

Tip

Adverbs **add** more information to a **verb**.

Adverbs answer the questions: **how**, **when** or **where** something happens.

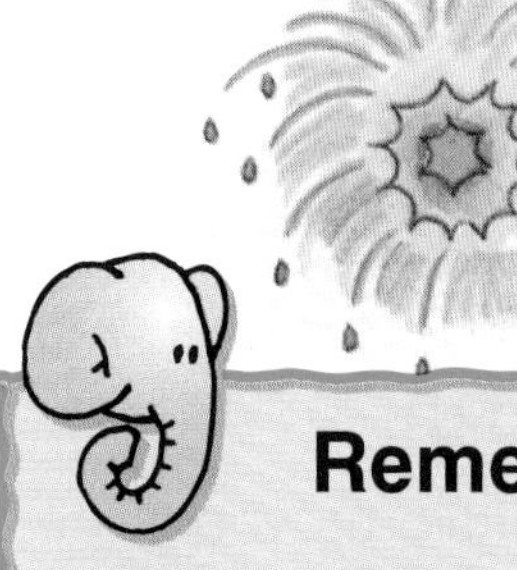

Remember

A **phrase** is a small group of words.

Sentence work

- To practise speech punctuation

Writing conversations

The mayor's words could be written:

"I declare this new sports centre open," announced the mayor proudly.

or

The mayor proudly announced, "I declare this new sports centre open."

1 Add the missing speech marks, commas and full stops to each of these sentences.

a I think I'd like to try the trampolines said Tara

b Tara said I think I'd like to try the trampolines

c Now we can go swimming whenever we like cried Sam excitedly

d Sam cried excitedly Now we can go swimming whenever we like

Tip

Look carefully at where the commas are put.

Notice how the speech marks are outside the full stops and commas.

2 The name of the speaker is in the middle of these sentences. Put in the missing speech marks, commas and full stops. The first one is done for you.

a I like swimming said Jim but I prefer bowling

"I like swimming," said Jim, "but I prefer bowling."

b When I go swimming said Jitendra my eyes get sore

c So do mine said Jim and it makes me look as if I've been crying

Words ending in *ey*

1 Look at the picture. List all the words you can find that end in ***ey***.

2 Write about the Grand Opening Fete at the Sports Centre, using words that end in ***ey***.

Word work

- To practise spelling some words ending in *ey*

Helpful words

hockey chutney trolley
alley abbey monkey
turkey key chimney
honey donkey valley

Plurals

When we make most words that end in ***y*** plural, we change the ***y*** to an ***i*** and add ***es***:

injury injuries

BUT if the word that ends in ***y*** has a vowel before it, we just add **s**:

alley alley<u>s</u>

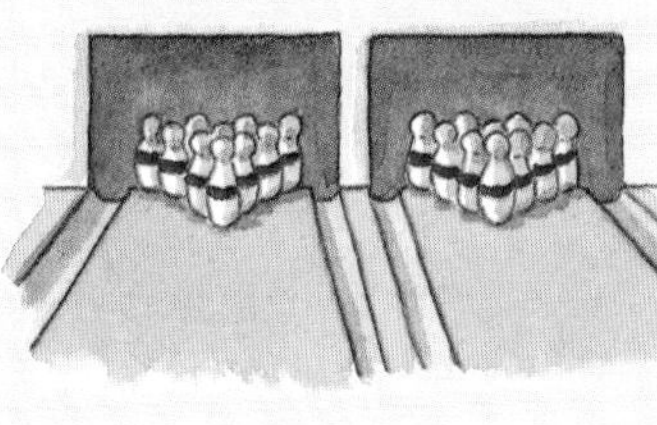

1 Write these words in their plural form:

fly lady country battery cry activity

2 Write these words in their plural form:

key valley toy trolley turkey day

Word work

- To learn the plural forms of words ending with a vowel + y

Remember

The **vowel letters** are ***a***, ***e***, ***i***, ***o***, ***u***.

Practising capitals with curves

B C D G J O P Q R S U

1 These are all the capital letters which have curves. Neatly copy them three times each.

2 Make a plan for a poster, using only capital letters, which will advertise your next school fete.

Handwriting

Camel Wrestling

Sentence work

- To practise word classes

The word machine

We have learnt about nouns, verbs, adjectives and adverbs.
Nouns are naming words.
Adjectives describe nouns.
Verbs are active or being words.
Adverbs usually describe verbs.

1 Write each of these words in a sentence.
Say whether you have used it as a **noun**, **verb**, **adjective** or **adverb**.

wrestled camel graceful
muzzle aggressive quickly

2 Copy this table. Write four words in each column.

Noun	Adjective	Verb	Adverb
competition	difficult	fighting	fiercely

Sentence work

- To revise word order and punctuation

What's missing?

Here is a letter to a camel owner from his family at home, but the camel chewed it before he could read it.

ar Laithe,
ad and I are you very mu
hope that your ca winning his matches.
Did you get him a new to stop
h other camel did it cost
you too mu ey? Let us know h
you want us to send to y

Lo om
and Dad

1 Copy the letter, but write in all the missing words and punctuation marks that the camel has eaten!

2 Pretend that you are Laithe. Write a letter back to your parents. You will need to make up an address.

Suffixes *able* and *ible*

Word work

- To learn how to use suffixes *able* and *ible*

Camels were valu**able** in Roman times.

When ***able*** or ***ible*** is added to most words ending in a single ***e***, the ***e*** is dropped and then the suffix added:

value + able = valu<u>able</u>

Remember

When we add a suffix to some words, the words themselves might need to make a change before the suffix is added.

1 Add the suffixes *able* or *ible* to these words:

sense + ible = 　　　　reason + able =

believe + able = 　　　　force + ible =

advise + able = 　　　　agree + able =

response + ible = 　　　　love + able =

2 Use a dictionary to check your answers.

Word work

- To learn more about homophones

Homophones

Remember, **homophones** are words that sound the same but are spelt differently and have different meanings.

Camel wrestling is great fun!

Please grate some cheese.

1 Copy these words and next to each one write a homophone. The first one is done to help you.

write right   rode   meet   fare   son

two   ewe   know   their   inn   sea

2 a Look through your reading book, or another book. Find ten homophones.

b Write a sentence that includes at least three words that are homophones.

Handwriting

able pattern

able able able able able able able able

1 Neatly copy the letter pattern in the box three times.

2 Neatly copy these words, adding the suffix *able* to each one. Like this:

comfort comfortable

suit   agree   depend   perish   notice   reason